Chaos in the Canopy

BRAVE
BOOKS

DOM-A-TRON

THE OLD ISLANDS

Doomsdome

Burrycanter

UTOPIA

Freedom Island

WIGGAMORE WOO

SUMA SAVANNA

Rushington

Hive H

Furenzy Park

Toke-A-Toke

Wonder Well

Capitol

Mushroom Village

Deserted Desert

Mt. Avalerif

RAKA RAIN FOREST

Sky Tree

Snapfast Meadow

CAR-A-LAGO COAST

Starlotte City

Gray Landing

Home of the Brave

Welcome to Freedom Island, Home of the Brave, where good battles evil and truth prevails. It's up to you to defend our great nation. Save the animals of Sky Tree by completing the BRAVE Challenge at the end of this book.

Watch this video for an introduction to the story and BRAVE Universe!

Saga Two: Iron Chaos
Book 10

Chaos in the Canopy

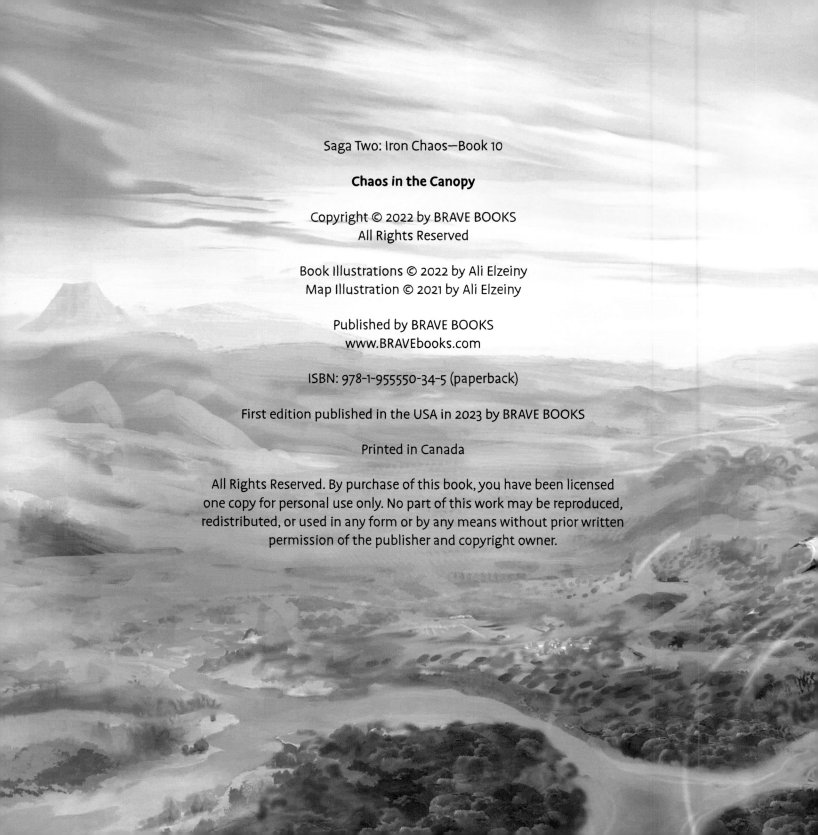

Saga Two: Iron Chaos—Book 10

Chaos in the Canopy

Copyright © 2022 by BRAVE BOOKS
All Rights Reserved

Book Illustrations © 2022 by Ali Elzeiny
Map Illustration © 2021 by Ali Elzeiny

Published by BRAVE BOOKS
www.BRAVEbooks.com

ISBN: 978-1-955550-34-5 (paperback)

First edition published in the USA in 2023 by BRAVE BOOKS

Printed in Canada

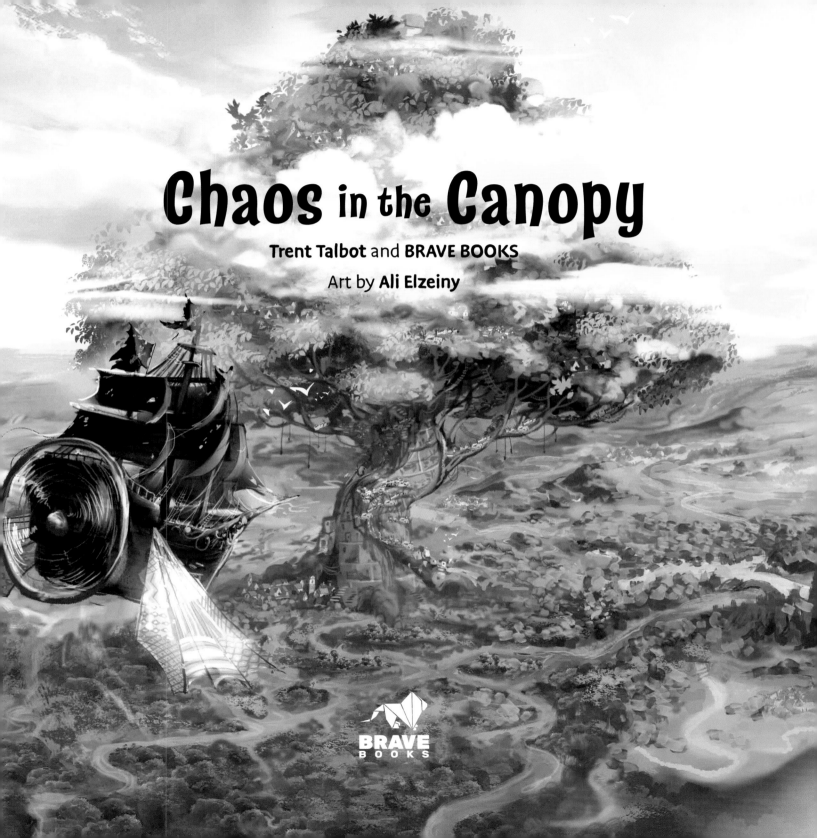

Chaos in the Canopy

Trent Talbot and **BRAVE BOOKS**

Art by **Ali Elzeiny**

BRAVE
BOOKS

Spruce the Sloth shook his head as he raised his poster high. This was not groovy at all.

Pirates were coming to chop down the legendary Sky Tree.

"You guys gotta chill out." Spruce
waved his poster at the pirate captain,
Lester. But Lester drowned him out
with the eerie sounds of his organ.

"Keep pumping the wings! Sharpen the saws!
You can't stop me with your weak little paws.
Load the cannons! Make them all flee!
Today's the day I'll destroy Sky Tree."

Spruce gave Sky Tree a big tight hug
and felt his heart sink.

MAKE TREES
NOT WAR

Then, from deep within the trunk,
Spruce heard the booming sound
of a gorilla's voice ...

"NOT GROOVY!"

Bongo and the rest of Team BRAVE burst into action, weapons pointed at the flying pirate ship.

"Bongo!" called Spruce. "Are you here to save the tree?"

"Absolutely!" Bongo loaded his cannon. "We'll do everything we can to keep the animals of Freedom Island safe."

Suddenly, all around them leaves burst into flames. The pirates were hurling flaming chili peppers at the tree.

"Goodness gracious!" cried Spruce, "This isn't what I meant when I said to chill!"

Spruce yelled, "Save the tree!" as Team BRAVE took off towards the danger.

But Team BRAVE was not focusing on putting out the fire. Instead, they were rushing into burning houses and pulling out animals.

"But the tree! It's burning!" Spruce shouted.

Team BRAVE whipped in and out, up and down, carting the animals to safety. As soon as the last one was out, Asher hooked his Mega-sprayer up to the water, and the team worked as one to douse the flames.

Spruce sighed in relief until he looked up ....

"Pirates!" he cried, "They're hurting the tree!"

Bats and wolves leapt onto the tree, hacking and slashing at anything and everything. They grinned and growled with menace.

"Lousy pirates! Make like a tree and leaf!" Bongo yelled, as they battled the pirates.

Spruce clung to a branch, tracking every moment with a wide-eyed gaze.

Spruce nearly fainted as he saw something unimaginable. It was uncooler than uncool. It was a straight up *bummer*.

Asher the fox raked a saw back and forth over a huge, beautiful limb.

Click

"What are you DOING?" cried Spruce.

"What are YOU doing?" cried Asher.

Spruce dove toward him, "You're supposed to be saving the tree!"

"I am!" Asher shouted as the sloth crashed into him.

"Oof! I need to use this limb if we're going to stop the pirates!"

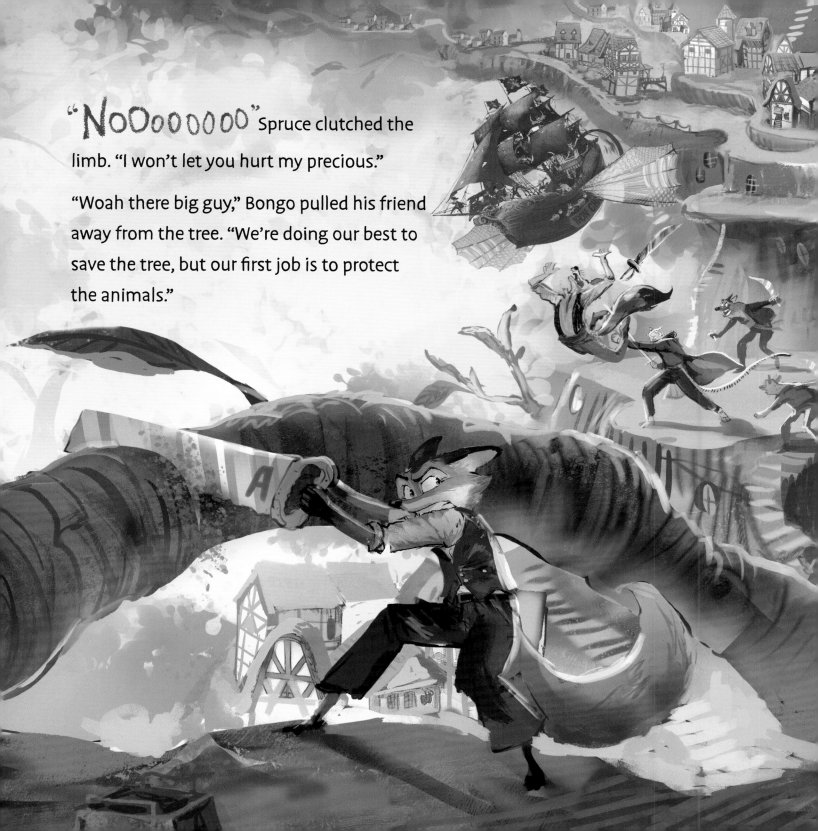

"NoOoooooo" Spruce clutched the limb. "I won't let you hurt my precious."

"Woah there big guy," Bongo pulled his friend away from the tree. "We're doing our best to save the tree, but our first job is to protect the animals."

"Hee Hee Hee!" Lester laughed. Before Spruce could say "Groovy gravy biscuits!" the pirates scooped him up in a piratey net. Lester banged on his organ and sang,

"I've got your friend, he's part of my cargo.
Just try to stop me, Asher and Bongo.
Now my final plan has come to pass.
Soon all of Sky Tree will feel my wrath!"

With a signal from Lester, the Iron Chaos went into action. Spruce helplessly looked on as huge saw blades began spinning, aimed at the tree.

"Work faster!" Bongo called. The whole team joined Asher, sawing down the limb.

Click!

With Asher's super-sized crossbow finished, Team BRAVE took their positions,

and launched flaming chili peppers right back at the oncoming pirate ship.

Bongo landed onto the Iron Chaos, pulled Spruce from the burning ship and kicked Lester directly into his own instrument.

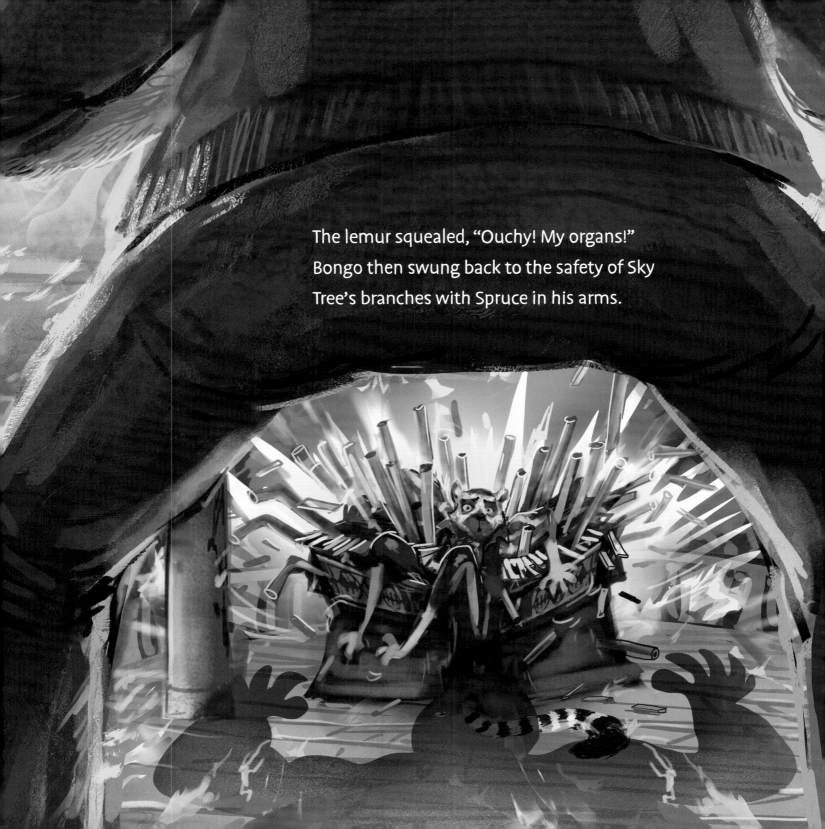

The lemur squealed, "Ouchy! My organs!"
Bongo then swung back to the safety of Sky
Tree's branches with Spruce in his arms.

"Dude." Spruce nodded his head. "That was a groovy rescue. Now I see why you needed to use Sky Tree's branch to save the animals and the rest of the tree."

"Sky Tree is very special," Bongo offered. "But we can always plant a new tree. We can't plant a new Spruce. You're irreplaceable, my friend."

Spruce smiled. "That's heavy, dude. I guess I should love trees because I love the friends who need them. If we left our friends in danger to save the tree, we'd have it all backwards, right?"

"Right on," Bongo grinned.

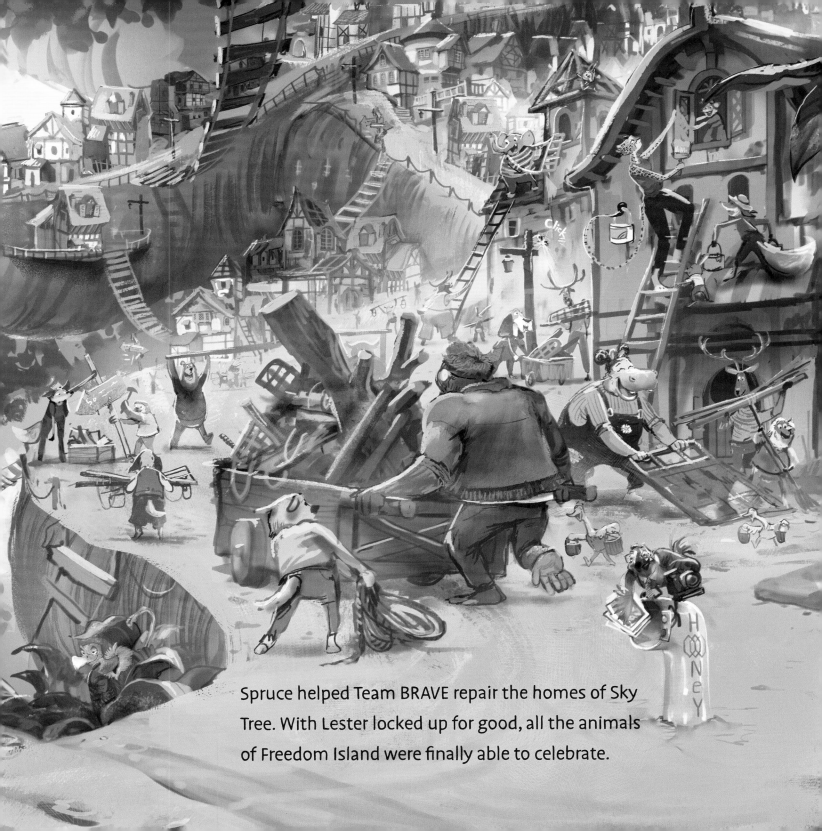

Spruce helped Team BRAVE repair the homes of Sky Tree. With Lester locked up for good, all the animals of Freedom Island were finally able to celebrate.

Far, far away, deep, deep in Doomsdome, an evil vulture fluttered. "Lester has failed," he squawked.

Black Heart smiled a thin, grim smile. "Lester was a fool. But just you wait. I have other plans for Team BRAVE."

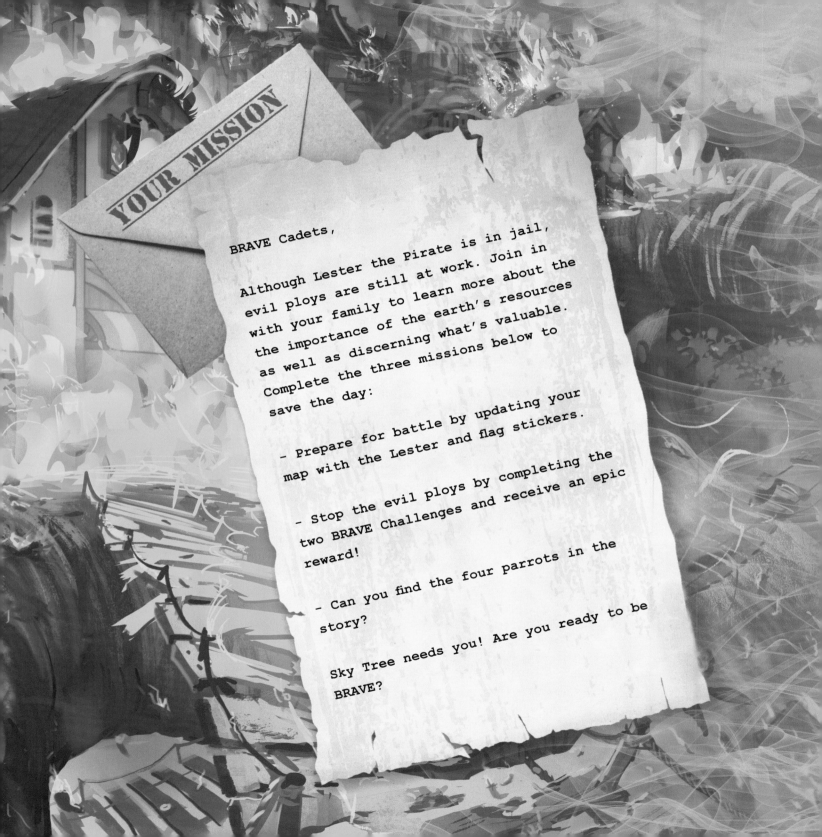

BRAVE Cadets,

Although Lester the Pirate is in jail, evil ploys are still at work. Join in with your family to learn more about the importance of the earth's resources as well as discerning what's valuable. Complete the three missions below to save the day:

- Prepare for battle by updating your map with the Lester and flag stickers.

- Stop the evil ploys by completing the two BRAVE Challenges and receive an epic reward!

- Can you find the four parrots in the story?

Sky Tree needs you! Are you ready to be BRAVE?

THE BRAVE CHALLENGE

INTRODUCING...
TRENT TALBOT

Trent Talbot is the CEO of BRAVE Books, as well as a medical doctor and father of two. Trent has a deep love for America and the values it was built upon. He wants to remind Americans of the beauty and importance of the land that God entrusted us with. He helped write this story and this BRAVE Challenge and will be popping in to help you explain these concepts to your children.

TRENT SUGGESTS:

"Conservationism says people have a responsibility to use and care for the environment and natural resources to benefit people today and future generations. Sometimes, people can prioritize the safety of the Earth more than the people living on it. And that is not right."

INTRODUCTION

Your mission for this BRAVE Challenge is to save the animals and Sky Tree from Lester and his pirate crew. To get started, grab a sheet of paper and a pencil, and draw a scoreboard like the one shown.

In the end, if your team scores more than the pirates, then you have won the challenge.

Before starting Game #1, choose a prize for winning. For example ...

- Build a birdhouse
- Go on a hike
- Having a picnic outside
- Whatever gets your kiddos excited!

BRAVE Cadets	Team Pirates
ЖЖ II	III

GAME #1 - EGGCELLENT RELAY!

LESSON

We can and should use the resources that God has given us.

OBJECTIVE

Team BRAVE is cutting down some of the branches of Sky Tree so they can defeat the pirates. BRAVE Cadets help Spruce realize they must use resources in order to save the animals of Sky Tree.

MATERIALS

An egg and spoon for each cadet and a die. (Or, substitute water balloons for eggs.)

INSTRUCTIONS

BRAVE TIP

Play this game outside

1. Have the cadets form a line on one side of the yard.
2. The cadets must take turns carrying an egg on a spoon across the yard and back.
3. Parents will place obstacles in the yard to make it harder for the cadets to get across.
4. The cadets must NOT touch any of the obstacles in the yard or else they must start over.
5. If any cadet drops the egg, they must start over. If the egg is completely broken, then they must grab a new egg.
6. Once they return to the starting point without touching any obstacles, have the cadet hand the egg to the next in line.

SCORING

- Roll the die to see the pirates' score.
- The cadets start with 8 points.
- The team loses 2 points every time a cadet drops an egg.
- They lose 1 point each time a cadet touches any obstacles.

TALK ABOUT IT

1. The eggs you used were fragile and needed to be protected in order to win the game. Are eggs an important resource? How so? What are other important resources?

2. If a resource is important, fragile, or valuable, does that mean we can't ever use it?

3. How did Spruce react to Asher cutting the tree in the story? Why did he react that way? What did Spruce value most based on his reaction?

4. Is it wrong to want to take care of the environment?

TRENT SUGGESTS:

"Absolutely not. God calls us to take care of the Earth, and make it a great place for us to live. We need to take care of the Earth in a way that benefits us as well."

"And God blessed them. And God said to them, "Be fruitful and multiply and fill the earth and subdue it, and have dominion over the fish of the sea and over the birds of the heavens and over every living thing that moves on the earth."

Genesis 1:28 (ESV)

5. How can you take care of the part of the world you interact with every day? (Think of examples, like picking up trash on your street.)

GAME #2 - OBSERVE THE WORTH!

LESSON
We must choose what is most valuable when faced with a hard decision.

OBJECTIVE
Spruce valued saving the tree over the animals. BRAVE Cadets, help Spruce realize what's more valuable to save!

MATERIALS
5 valuable items and 5 non-valuable items (both kept secret).

INSTRUCTIONS

BRAVE TIP
Parents, read the instructions before explaining the game to the cadets. Make sure the cadets do NOT see the items you gather!

1. *Secret Step: Parents, gather 5 items that have significant value, at least one of which has only sentimental value, which you will save for the last round. Then gather five everyday items that are cheap and relatively worthless (for example, a pencil, a coaster, or a magnet off the fridge).*

2. Place a valuable item and a non-valuable item next to each other on a table. Keep the other items hidden from the cadets.

3. The cadets must, as a team, decide which object holds more value, voting if they can't agree.

4. Once they have made a decision, tell them the correct answer, and reveal the next 2 items.

5. For the last round, have the cadets compare one item of sentimental value, but little to no monetary worth, with an item that may be expensive but has little true value.

SCORING

- Every time the cadets guess correctly, award them 1 point.
- For every incorrect guess, award the pirates 1 point.

TALK ABOUT IT

1. In the game, you had to decide which items had the most value. Was it hard to decide which was more valuable? Why?

2. Do you think an item holds the same value for everyone? Why or why not?

3. In the story, Spruce wanted Team BRAVE to protect the tree? What is more valuable than the tree?

4. How did Spruce learn that the animals were more valuable than the tree?

5. Name an object that's important to you. Would you be upset if your sibling or friend broke it? How do you think that you would respond if that happened? Can you fix or replace the object? Can you replace your sibling or friend?

TRENT SUGGESTS:

"It's hard to give up something that we find valuable in order to serve someone else. But when we give up our own desires, we model godly characteristics that can be a good example to those around us for Christ. Philippians 2:4 says, 'Let each of you look not only to his own interests, but also to the interests of others.'"

6. Can you think of a time where you valued an object more than a person? Have you ever not wanted to share a toy? When you refuse to share, what are you valuing most?

TALLY UP THE POINTS TO SEE IF YOU WON!

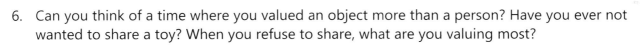

FINAL THOUGHTS FROM TRENT TALBOT

Conservationism is the belief that humans are meant to take care of the earth and use its resources for the benefit of humans. Environmentalism has a tendency to turn that on its head and say that humans exist to serve and protect the earth. It's important for us to realize that the resources we have are a gift from God and that we should use them to glorify him. Ultimately, people and the rest of creation all exist to glorify him. That's why we strive to use the resources God has entrusted to us carefully and why we prioritize the wellbeing of people, who bear God's image. When we exercise dominion over the world to bless people like God commanded, we bring glory to his name!